Piano Exam Pieces

ABRSM Grade 1

Selected from the 2021 & 2022 syllabus

Name

Date of exam

M000159583

Contents

Editor for ABRSM: Richard Jones

Other pieces for Grade 1

Published in 2020 by ABRSM (Publishing) Ltd, a wholly owned subsidiary of ABRSM, 4 London Wall Place, London EC2Y 5AU, United Kingdom

© 2020 by The Associated Board of the Royal Schools of Music Distributed worldwide by Oxford University Press

Music origination by Julia Bovee

Cover by Kate Benjamin & Andy Potts, with thanks to Brighton College

Printed in England by Halstan & Co. Ltd, Amersham, Bucks., on materials from sustainable sources.

P15058

A Toy

No. 193 from *Fitzwilliam Virginal Book, Vol. 2*

Adaptation by Richard Jones

Anon.

This piece is taken from the *Fitzwilliam Virginal Book*, a collection of English keyboard music copied out between 1606 and 1619. It contains nearly 300 pieces by English composers. A 'toy' is a light piece for lute or virginals (small harpsichord) from the late 16th or early 17th century. Another version of this piece appears later in the Fitzwilliam book where it is called 'Coranto', which means 'running'. This probably refers to the running figures in bars 1 and 5 and elsewhere in the piece. It also points to the dance-like character of the music.

Source: Cambridge, Fitzwilliam Museum, Mu. MS 168. In the version printed here, all dynamics, slurs and staccatos are editorial. In bars 12–14 the source has F♮ in place of F♯, presumably in error.

© 2020 by The Associated Board of the Royal Schools of Music

Minuet in C

K. 6

A:2

W. A. Mozart
(1756–91)

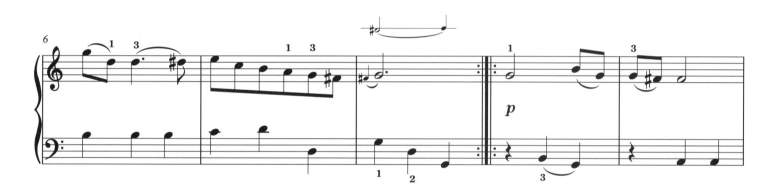

Wolfgang Amadeus Mozart is thought to have written this piece in Brussels in October 1763, when he was seven years old. His father Leopold added this Minuet to a collection that he had started to make in 1759 for his eight-year-old daughter Maria Anna (known as Nannerl), the elder sister of Wolfgang Amadeus. At that time Leopold was teaching Nannerl to play the piano. Wolfgang learnt pieces from his sister's book when he was only four. Some of his earliest compositions are modelled on pieces he found there, and no doubt played himself.

Source: L. Mozart: *Nannerl-Notenbuch*, 1759; original MS, property of the Internationale Stiftung Mozarteum, Salzburg. This piece is in Leopold Mozart's hand and entitled 'Menuet'. In this edition, all slurs are drawn from the source, except that of bar 4, which is editorial. Also editorial are all dynamics, the sharp to *d″* in bar 4, and the appoggiatura in bar 16 (cf. bar 8).

4

A:3

Parson's Farewell

from *The English Dancing Master*

Arranged by David Blackwell

Trad. English

This piece is a traditional English country dance for couples. It was published by John Playford, a 17th-century London music publisher, in *The English Dancing Master* (1651), one of his most well-known collections of music.

In the exam, the repeat should be played.

Melodie

No. 1 from *Album für die Jugend*, Op. 68

B:1

Robert Schumann
(1810–56)

Robert Schumann composed his *Album für die Jugend* (Album for the Young) in less than a month in 1848. At the time, the composer wrote: 'I don't remember ever having been in such good musical form … the pieces simply poured out, one after another.' Some of the 42 pieces in the collection were dedicated to Schumann's daughter Marie on her seventh birthday.

At the first right-hand note of bars 5–7 etc., an accent sign would not have been suited to the smooth, singing style of the music, so Schumann writes a sign that implies a gentle emphasis, rather than an attack.

Source: *43* [sic] *Clavierstücke für die Jugend*, Op. 68 (Hamburg: Schuberth & Co., 1850). The opening dynamic and the hairpins are original. All other dynamics are editorial suggestions only.

Adapted from Schumann: *Album für die Jugend*, Op. 68, edited by Howard Ferguson (ABRSM)

B:2

The Swing

from *Through the Windowpane*

Chee-Hwa Tan
(born 1965)

Chee-Hwa Tan is a Malaysian pianist, teacher and composer. She emigrated to the USA in 1984 and is now head of piano tuition at the Lamont School of Music, University of Denver, Colorado.

'The Swing' is inspired by the poem of that name from *A Child's Garden of Verses* by Robert Louis Stevenson. Here is the first verse of the poem:

How do you like to go up in a swing,
Up in the air so blue?
Oh, I do think it the pleasantest thing
Ever a child can do!

Down by the salley gardens

B:3

Arranged by David Blackwell

Trad. Irish

The poem 'Down by the salley gardens' is by the Irish poet W. B. Yeats. It was set to this traditional Irish tune by Herbert Hughes in 1909. Here is the first verse of the poem:

> Down by the salley gardens my love and I did meet;
> She passed the salley gardens with little snow-white feet.
> She bid me take love easy, as the leaves grow on the tree;
> But I, being young and foolish, with her would not agree.

The 'salley gardens' of the first line are a plantation of willow trees.

* The arranger, David Blackwell, says: 'To begin, press the left-hand notes down *silently* (indicated here by diamond-shaped noteheads) and then start the melody when you're ready. Listen to the tune and make it as beautiful as you can – imagine you're a singer!'

© 2020 by The Associated Board of the Royal Schools of Music

C:1

Cockatoo

No. 9 from *Very Easy Little Peppers*

Elissa Milne
(born 1967)

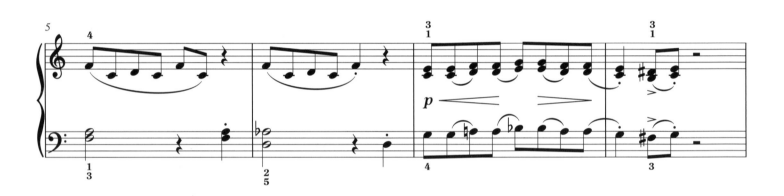

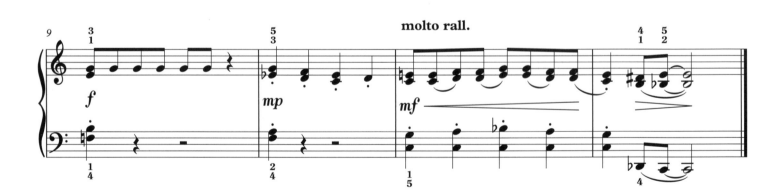

Elissa Milne studied composition at the University of Auckland, New Zealand. She is now based in Sydney, Australia, where she teaches piano and specialises in composing educational piano music. Here she presents a sound picture of the cockatoo, an Australian species of parrot that comes across as a stubborn and persistent creature. Although the composer's metronome mark is ♩ = 126–138, students may prefer a slower tempo, for example ♩ = *c*.116.

Grasshopper

Szöcske

No. 15 from *22 Kis Zongoradarab*

C:2

Lajos Papp
(1935–2019)

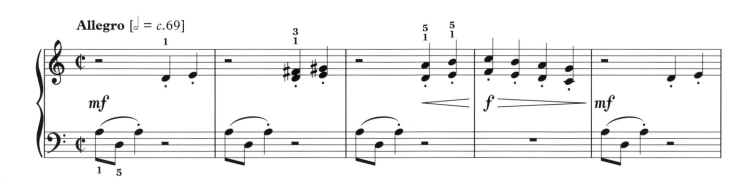

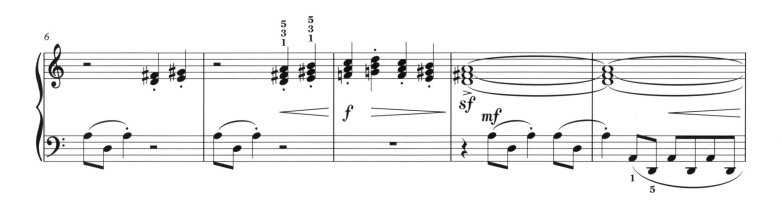

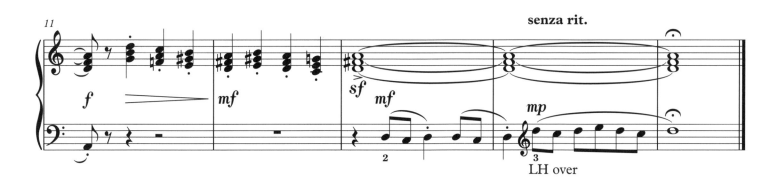

Lajos Papp was a Hungarian composer and music educator who studied at the Budapest Academy (1954–60). He then taught piano and theory at the Music School in Budapest. He emigrated to Oldenburg, Germany, in 1973. This piece is taken from his *22 Kis Zongoradarab* (22 Little Piano Pieces), which was written in 1985.

C:3

The Detective

No. 6 from *Up-Grade!* Piano Grades 1–2

Pam Wedgwood
(born 1947)

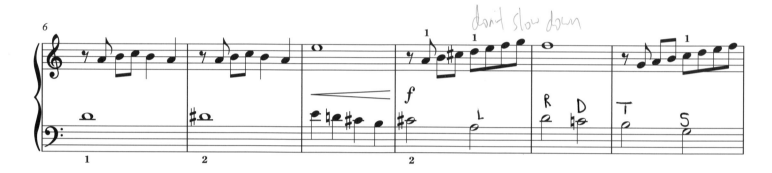

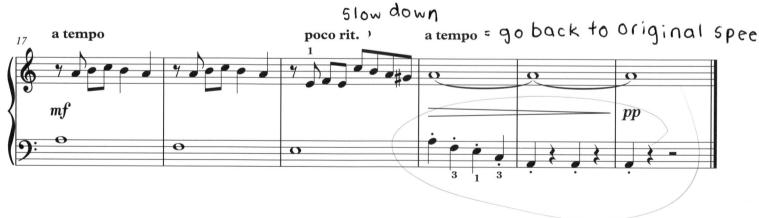

Pam Wedgwood studied at Trinity College of Music in London, after which she became an orchestral horn player. For many years she has concentrated on instrumental teaching and has composed several highly successful series of educational pieces, including *Jazzin' About* and *Up-Grade!*

ABRSM Aural

A: Tap the pulse of music & say if it is in 2 or 3

B. Sing as an echo 3 short phrases

C. Recognize a rythmic change & describe it

D. Identify features of music
  - dynamics (p/f)
  - gradation of tone (cresc/decresc)
  - articulation (stacc/legato)

ABRSM Aural

A: Tap the pulse of music & say if it is in 2 or 3

B. Sing as an echo 3 short phrases